Four Seasons

1. Earth has four seasons. List the four seasons.

    1 _____

    2 _____

    3 _____

    4 _____

2. List as many different types of weather as you can. You could draw pictures as well as writing words.

Recording Weather

1   Draw a picture to show what the weather is today.

2   Find out what the weather is like in England today. Draw a picture to show the weather.

3   Which type of weather do you like best? Why?

I like _____ weather because

_____

Changing Seasons

4a Draw your own weather symbols for different types of weather.

4b Write the type of weather under each weather symbol.

Measuring Rainfall

This chart shows that in England it rains every month. How much does it rain where you live?

Rainfall in England	Months
Little	May, June, July
Some	February, March, April, August, September
Lots	January, October, November, December

1   Record rainfall in the chart for where you live.

Rainfall in _____	Months
None	
Little	
Some	
Lots	

Measuring Temperature

Amil's mother measures the temperature of his bath water with a thermometer to be sure the water is not too hot.

1. Draw two pictures showing when we use a thermometer. Explain why it is being used.

The Wind

Some toys only work when it is windy.

1. Look at the diagrams of different toys. Tick the ones that need the wind to work.

Science Skills

Measure it!

A wind toy can be used to measure the wind.

1   Draw pictures in the table below.

Wind strength	Streamer toy
No wind	
Gentle	
Medium	
Strong	

Day Length

1a Record the times for sunset and sunrise today where you live.

1b Draw a picture and write to show what you were doing at these times.

Sunrise was at _____ in the morning.

I was _____.

Sunset was at _____ in the evening.

I was _____.

Changing Day Length

Class 1 live in England. They have been recording whether it is dark or light when they go to bed and get up at different times of the year.

1   Record these for where you live.

Time of year	England	England	_____	_____
	Go to bed	Get up	Go to bed	Get up
Winter	Dark	Dark		
Spring	Dark	Light		
Summer	Light	Light		
Autumn	Light	Dark		

2   How are yours different from Class 1's in England?

_____

_____

_____

Observing the Weather

We can make a simple weather station. We need to measure temperature, wind strength and rainfall.

1. Draw pictures of what you would use.
2. Record what they measure.

My weather station

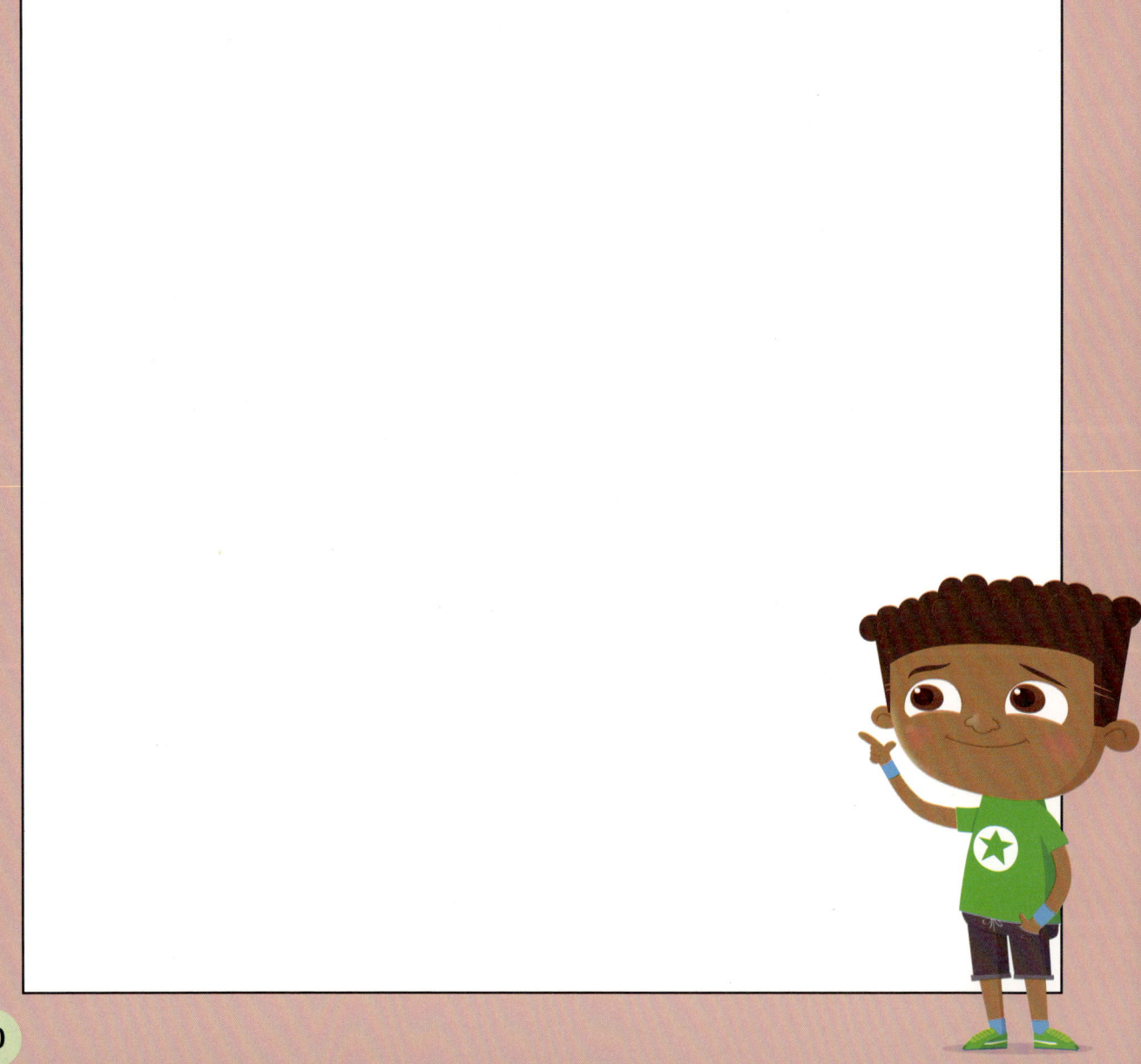

Science Skills

Observe it!

Class 1 have been using their weather station. This table shows what they found out.

Date	Wind strength	Temperature	Rainfall
8th January	no wind	cold	3 cm
7th April	gentle	warm	1 cm
10th July	gentle	hot	0 cm
9th October	strong	warm	2 cm

Use the table to answer these questions.

1 When was there no wind?

   _____

2 Which day was best to fly a kite?

   _____

3 When was it hot?

   _____

4 When would you need a warm coat?

   _____

5 How much more did it rain on 8th January than on 7th April?

   _____

Differences Between Seasons

In England there are big differences in weather and day length in the different seasons.

1   **Find out about the seasons in another place where the weather is not always the same. Make a poster for each season in that place.**

Spring in _____

Changing Seasons

Summer in _____

Differences Between Seasons

Autumn in _____

Changing Seasons

Winter in _____

2 Tell a classmate how the seasons in England are different from where you live.

What do we Know?

Imagine an aunt has come from England to stay for a year.

1a To remind her of her home draw a picture of what you think her garden could look like in summer.

1b Then draw it in winter.

1c Draw weather symbols next to each picture to show the type of weather.

Garden in the summer

Garden in the winter